DREAMLAND

Learn with
PHONICS

DOUBLE-LETTER CONSONANT SOUNDS

BOOK 4

Author
Lata Seth

Published by

DREAMLAND PUBLICATIONS

J-128, KIRTI NAGAR, NEW DELHI - 110 015 (INDIA)
Ph. : 011-2543 5657, 2510 6050 Fax. : 011-2543 8283
E-mail : dreamland@vsnl.com
www.dreamlandpublications.com

Published in 2014 by
DREAMLAND PUBLICATIONS
J-128, Kirti Nagar, New Delhi - 110 015 (India)
Tel : 011-2510 6050, Fax : 011-2543 8283
E-mail : dreamland@vsnl.com, www.dreamlandpublications.com
ISBN : 978-93-5089-533-7
Printed by
Haploos Printing House

Preface

Phonics is a method of teaching how to read using the sounds that letters represent. This series is a set of 5 books beginning with sounds connected with 26 letters of the English alphabet, short and long vowels and progressing to letter blends. The series has been especially designed for young learners aged 3 to 7 to help them become good readers. Words represented with pictures enhance and encourage independent learning and strengthen the spelling skills. A variety of exercises and engaging activities offer essential practice and inspire young learners to test what they have learnt. These workbook-based phonics books are recommended for young learners as well as teachers and parents who want to teach their children the art of reading.

Contents

1	Introduction	5
2	bl-, cl-, fl-	6-15
3	gl-, pl-, sl-	16-24
4	br-, cr-, fr-	25-33
5	dr-, gr-, pr-, tr-	34-42
6	Let Us Revise 1 (Chapters 1-4)	43-47
7	sm-, sn-, st-, sw-	48-56
8	-nt, -nk, -ng, -ck	57-65
9	ch-, -ch, sh-, -sh	66-74
10	th-, -th, ph-, -ph, wh-	75-83
11	Let Us Revise 2 (Chapters 5-8)	84-88
12	Let Us Review	89-96

Order of Lessons

Introduction

1

bl-

cl-

fl-

2

gl-

pl-

sl-

3

br-

cr-

fr-

4

dr-

gr-

pr-

tr-

Let Us Revise 1 (Chapters 1-4)

	sm-	sn-	st-	sw-
5				
	-nt	-nk	-ng	-ck
6				
	ch-	-ch	sh-	-sh
7				
	th-	-th	ph-	-ph	wh-
8				

Let Us Revise 2 (Chapters 5-8)
Let Us Review

Introduction

In this book, we will learn the blends. Children will be taught the sounds produced using two consonant letters together.

Hi!
what are we going to learn in this book?

Word families are groups of words having a common pattern. They consist of the same combinations of letters in them and a similar sound. For example, *blue, blade* and *blind* are a family of words with the 'bl' sound and a common letter combination.

bl- cl- fl-

In this chapter, we will read about two consonant clusters bl-, cl- and fl-.

Read loudly and listen to the two consonant cluster sounds.

bl + ue = blue   **cl + own = clown**   **fl + ea = flea**

 Here are some more new words for you.

bl-

blade   blow   block   blind

cl-

clap   clock   clip   cloth

fl-

flower   flown   florist   flute

Time to Solve

Look at the pictures and tick the cluster-sounds that the word begins with.

bl-

cl-

cl-

fl-

bl-

fl-

cl-

bl-

cl-

fl-

fl-

cl-

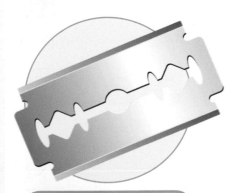

Look at the pictures and circle their correct names.

flute | flea

block | blow

clip | clock

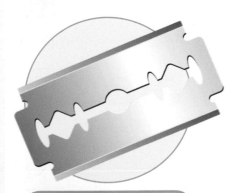

blind | blade

flea | flown

clap | clown

Circle the word not matching with the word-sound in its group.

florist

flute

blue

block

flea

blow

blind

clown

clock

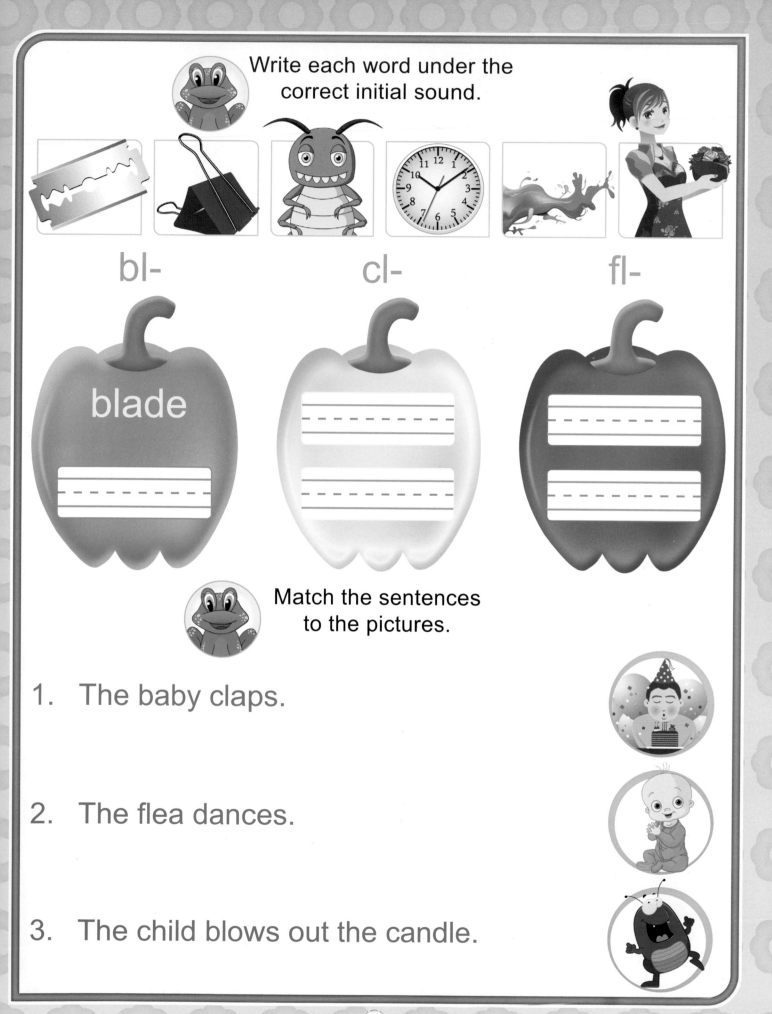

Write each word under the
correct initial sound.

bl-   cl-   fl-

blade

Match the sentences
to the pictures.

1. The baby claps.

2. The flea dances.

3. The child blows out the candle.

Read the question and tick the correct option.
Then write the answer on the line.

What does a child have in his hand?

1 ----block----

blade

block

What is on the wall?

2

cloth

clock

What is the man playing?

3

flute

flower

Circle the bl-, cl- and fl- words and
write them also.

The (blue) block

1 blue

The clip on the cloth

2

The florist with flowers

3

Fill in the blanks and look at the pictures for clues.

1. The girl has a **blue** dress.

2. The _____ makes us laugh.

3. The _____ is very beautiful.

 Find the words in the boxes and write them. Look at the pictures for clues. One has been done for you.

| b | l | o | w | z | w |

------- **blow** -------

| w | a | c | l | a | p |

| r | e | f | l | e | a |

Look at the pictures and find their names in the crossword.

b	l	a	d	e	f	c	a
o	c	k	u	b	l	l	o
f	l	u	t	e	c	o	u
l	d	c	e	l	d	c	l
e	b	k	a	b	u	k	b
a	e	b	l	u	e	a	d

Time to Chant

Blow the candles, and clap, clap, clap!

Clip the clothes, before they flap, flap, flap!

Flies the flea, go trap, trap, and trap!

Sight Words — a, has, in, his, from, the, for

A florist has many beautiful
flowers in his shop.

A clown picks some blue
flowers from his shop.

The clown plays the flute
for the florist.

The florist claps
for the clown.

Do at Home

Tick the word-group / sentence that describes the picture.

1  ☑ The flower on the cloth

☐ The flower on the clip

2  ☐ The clown with the clock

☐ The clown with the block

3  ☐ The florist plays a flute.

☐ The florist plays a blade.

4  ☐ The man wears a blue coat.

☐ The man wears a red coat.

5  ☐ The children clap.

☐ The children dance.

gl- pl- sl-

In this chapter, we will read about two consonant clusters gl-, pl- and sl-.

Read loudly and listen to the two consonant cluster sounds.

gl + ue = glue   pl + ay = play   sl + ed = sled

 Here are some more new words for you.

gl-

glide   glass   globe   glove

pl-

plant   plane   plate   plug

sl-

sleep   slip   slide   slice

Time to Solve

Look at the pictures and tick the
cluster-sounds that the word begins with.

gl-

sl-

gl-

pl-

sl-

gl-

gl-

sl-

pl-

sl-

gl-

sl-

Look at the pictures and circle
their correct names.

plane	plant
glue	globe
sled	sleep

glove	glue
sled	slice
plate	plant

Circle the word not matching with the word-sound in its group.

glide

play

glove

plug

slide

plant

slide

glue

slip

Write each word under the
correct initial sound.

gl-   pl-   sl-

Match the sentences
to the pictures.

1. The sled is on the snow.

2. The plant is in the pot.

3. The boy is fixing the glass with glue.

Read the question and tick the correct option.
Then write the answer on the line.

1 What is on the table?

_____

- - - - - - - - - - - - - - - - - -

glue

globe

2 The boy is repairing what?

_____

- - - - - - - - - - - - - - - - - -

plug

plate

3 The girl is on what?

_____

- - - - - - - - - - - - - - - - - -

slice

sled

Circle the gl-, pl- and sl- words
and write them also.

1 The globe on the glass

_____

- - - - - - - - - - - - - - - - - -

2 The plug on a plate

_____

- - - - - - - - - - - - - - - - - -

3 The children slip and slide

_____

- - - - - - - - - - - - - - - - - -

Fill in the blanks and look at the pictures for clues.

1. The girl has a _____ on her hand.

2. The man is watering a _____

3. This mango _____ is very tasty.

Find the words in the boxes and write them. Look at the pictures for clues.

g	l	u	e	y	q

- -

w	p	l	a	y	e

- -

r	g	s	l	i	p

- -

Time to Chant

Slip and slide, slip and slide, on the ice, let us glide!

Mango slice, mango slice, on the plate, with some ice!

Glue and globe, glue and globe, on the glass, with the glove!

Story Time

Read this story aloud.

Sight Words — a, has, the, with

A girl has a nice
doll-house.

Her friend breaks the
doll-house by mistake.

She takes glue and
fixes the doll-house.

The girls play with
the doll-house.

Do at Home

Tick the word-group / sentence that describes the picture.

1 ☐ The girl with the white gloves

☐ The girl with the red gloves

2 ☐ A slice of mango on the plate

☐ A slice of apple on the plate

3 ☐ The girl slips on a banana peel.

☐ The girl slides on a banana peel.

4 ☐ The glass is black.

☐ The glass is white.

5 ☐ The boy plays with the plane.

☐ The boy plays with the plug.

br- cr- fr-

In this chapter, we will read about two consonant clusters br-, cr- and fr-.

Read loudly and listen to the two consonant cluster sounds.

br + ide = bride   cr + ow = crow   fr + uit = fruit

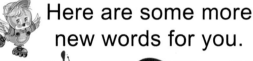 Here are some more new words for you.

 br-

brown   brave   broom   branch

 cr-

crab   crate   cross   crane

fr-

frog   friend   frame   frown

Time to Solve

Look at the pictures and tick the cluster-sounds that the word begins with.

- br-
- cr-

- cr-
- fr-

- br-
- fr-

- cr-
- br-

- fr-
- cr-

- fr-
- br-

 Look at the pictures and circle their correct names.

brave branch

crate crane

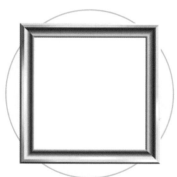

frog frame

crane crate

fruit frown

brown broom

Circle the word not matching
with the word-sound in its group.

brown   frog   branch

frown   friend   crate

cross   broom   crab

Write each word under the
correct initial sound.

br-

cr-

fr-

 Match the sentences
to the pictures.

1.   The girl has a brown broom.

2.   The crab is on the crate.

3.   The frog is eating the fruit.

**Read the question and tick the correct option.
Then write the answer on the line.**

The girl is sweeping the floor with what?

1 _____

broom

cross

Who is climbing the branch?

2 _____

crab

frog

The crab has a what?

3 _____

fruit

frame

**Circle the br-, cr- and fr- words
and write them also.**

The brown branch

1 _____

The crab on the crate

2 _____

MILK

The frog with a crown

3 _____

Fill in the blanks and look at the pictures for clues.

1. The boy is very _____.

2. The _____ is lifting the crate.

3. There is my photo in the _____.

 Find the words in the boxes and write them. Look at the pictures for clues.

u	b	r	i	d	e

- - - - - - - - - - - - - - - - - - -

w	c	r	o	s	s

- - - - - - - - - - - - - - - - - - -

h	t	f	r	o	g

- - - - - - - - - - - - - - - - - - -

Time to Chant

"Croak, croak", says the frog, friends are hard to come along.

"Caw, caw", says the crow, crane is ready for the tow.

"Sweet, sweet", is the bride, brave groom is taking pride.

Story Time

Read this story aloud.

Sight Words — the, and, are, for, to, they, see

The crab, the crow and the frog
are looking for something to eat.

They see some ripe fruits on a
branch of a tree.

The crow drops the fruit
on the ground.

The crow, the crab and the
frog share the fruit happily.

Do at Home

Tick the word-group / sentence that describes the picture.

1.
☐ The bride is in the white dress.
☐ The bride is in the yellow dress.

2.
☐ The two girls are friends.
☐ The two boys are friends.

3.
☐ The apple is on the frog.
☐ The frog is on the apple.

4.
☐ The crab has a broom.
☐ The crab has a frame.

5.
☐ The crow is sitting on the crane.
☐ The crow is sitting on the branch.

4

dr- gr- pr- tr-

In this chapter, we will read about two consonant clusters dr-, gr-, pr- and tr-.

Read loudly and listen to the two consonant cluster sounds.

(dr + um = drum) (gr + ape = grape) (pr + ince = prince) (tr + unk = trunk)

Here are some more new words for you.

-dr
 drink
 dragon
 draw
 drive

-gr
 green
 grab
 grass
 groom

-pr
 prize
 present
 price
 pray

-tr
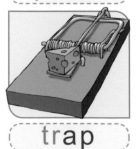 trap
 truck
 tray
 tree

Time to Solve

Look at the pictures and tick the cluster-sounds that the word begins with.

 dr- / tr-

 pr- / gr-

 pr- / tr-

 tr- / sl-

 dr- / tr-

 tr- / gr-

Look at the pictures and circle their correct names.

 drive **drink**

 grab **grass**

 prize **pray**

 trap **tree**

 price **prince**

draw **drink**

Circle the word not matching with the word-sound in its group.

dragon   draw   grab

grass   price   grape

pray   present   drink

groom   trap   truck

Write each word under the
correct initial sound.

dr-

tr-

gr-

pr-

Match the sentences
to the pictures.

1. The dragon beat the drum.

2.   The grapes are green.

3. The prince is praying.

4. The big trunk.

Read the question and tick the correct option.
Then write the answer on the line.

1 The dragon does what?
_____
- -
_____

drive

draw

2 The snake crawls on what?
_____
- -
_____

grass

grape

3 The boy is looking at what?
_____
- -
_____

prize

price

4 The rat is caught in a what?
_____
- -
_____

trap

truck

Circle the gr-, pr- and tr- words
and also write them.

1 The green grass
_____
- -
_____

2 The price on the present
_____
- -
_____

3 The trunk on a tree
_____
- -
_____

Fill in the blanks and look at the pictures for clues.

1.　The girl likes to _____.

2.　The _____ lives in the palace.

3.　Open the _____.

　Find the words in the boxes and write them. Look at the pictures for clues.

| r | d | r | i | v | e |

| r | i | g | r | a | b |

| q | p | r | a | y | z |

| t | r | e | e | a | r |

Time to Chant

They grow together in a bunch, green grapes are juicy to munch,

The prince takes them for brunch,

They are the dragon's favourite lunch,

"Grab the tray" says the groom,

"And eat the grapes — crunch, crunch, and crunch!"

Story Time

Read this story aloud.

The prince holds a musical contest in his palace.

The dragon plays the drum.

The prince gives the dragon a prize and other presents.

The dragon carries the prize and presents.

Do at Home

Tick the word-group / sentence that describes the picture.

1

☐ The boy is playing the drum.

☐ The girl is playing the drum.

2

☐ The groom is driving the car.

☐ The groom is driving the truck.

3

☐ The girl got a present.

☐ The girl got a prize.

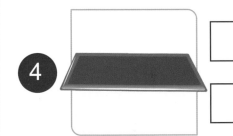

4

☐ The tray is full of sweets.

☐ The tray is empty.

5

☐ The children have won the prize.

☐ The children have won the present.

Let Us Revise 1

Chapters 1-4

Look at the pictures and tick
the correct initial sounds.

 bl- / fl-

 tr- / pr-

 br- / cr-

 gl- / pl-

 cl- / sl-

 gr- / fr-

 See the picture and circle the correct word.

 flower   flute

 glass   globe

 branch   brave

 truck   trunk

 dragon   drive

 clip   cloth

Draw a line to complete the word.
Look at the picture for clue.
Write the word also.

fl	ave	**flea**
gl	ize	
sl	uck	
br	uit	
pr	ate	
tr	ea	
fr	ue	
pl	ed	

Fill in the blanks by choosing the correct option.

 The bride is marrying the _____ . (groom / clown)

 The children _____ down the ice. (slip / slide)

 The man is selling _____ . (fruits / flowers)

 The boy is looking at the _____ . (clock / globe)

 The crow is sitting on a _____ . (tree / trunk)

Find the answers to these riddles matching them to the pictures.

1   It is very sharp. It is used to cut things. What is it?

2   It is used to tell the time. What is it?

3   It is black. It is a bird. What is it?

 Tick the sentence that describes the picture.

☐ The blind man has a flower.

☐ The blind man has a flute.

☐ The boy plays with the plane.

☐ The boy plays with the broom.

☐ He drives the truck.

☐ He drives the crane.

Fill in the missing words choosing the two consonant clusters from the box to complete each story.

cr-, fr-, pr-

The .....ab wanted to cross the lake. He asked the .....og to carry him. So, the .....og helped him. They became good .....iends. The .....ab gave the .....og a .....esent.

br-, cl-, dr-, pr-

There lived a .....agon. Everyone feared him. The .....ave .....ince killed him. Everyone .....apped for the .....ince.

sm- sn- st- sw-

In this chapter, we will read about two consonant clusters sm-, sn-, st- and sw-.

Read loudly and listen to the two consonant cluster sounds.

| sm + oke = smoke | sn + ow = snow | st + eam = steam | sw + an = swan |

 Here are some more new words for you.

sm-

smell   smile   small   smart

sn-

snack   sniff   snail   snake

st-

stew   story   stove   stamp

sw-

swim   swing   sweep   sweet

Time to Solve

Look at the pictures and tick the
cluster-sounds that the word begins with.

sm-

sn-

st-

sm-

sn-

sw-

sm-

sw-

st-

sw-

sm-

sn-

Look at the pictures and circle
their correct names.

sweep | sweet

stamp | stew

smoke | smile

snow | snail

sweet | sweep

story | stove

Circle the word not matching with the word-sound in its group.

smell   stamp   small

sweep   snake   snail

stew   smile   stove

swim   swing   story

 Write the words under the correct initial sound.

sn-   **sm-**

                  sw-   **st-**

 Match the sentences to the pictures.

1.   Smoke comes out of the chimney.

2.   The dog sniffs the food.

3.   The stew boils.

4.   The child swims.

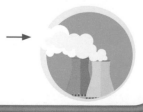

Read the question and tick the correct option.
Then write the answer on the line.

What is coming out of the house?

1 _____

smoke

small

The boy is eating what?

2 _____

snake

snack

The woman is looking at what?

3 _____

stew

steam

On what the girl is sitting?

4 _____

swim

swing

Circle the sm-, sn- and st- words
and write them also.

The small girl smiles.

1 _____

The dog sniffs the snack.

2 _____

The stew is on the stove.

3 _____

Fill in the blanks and look at the pictures for clues.

1. The boy likes to _____ .

2. The stove is giving out _____ .

3. The children are playing in the _____ .

Find the words in the boxes and write them. Look at the pictures for clues.

| q | s | m | i | l | e |

_____

| r | s | n | o | w | b |

_____

| s | t | e | w | y | z |

_____

| d | w | s | w | i | m |

_____

Time to Chant

The girl tells a story, the snake hears the story,

The snail hears the story, the swan hears the story,

The dog hears the story, then they all smile,

And go for a swim.

Story Time

Read this story aloud.

Sight Words — is, a, to, his, it, and, on, the, of

Grandpa is telling
his grandson a story.

It begins to snow outside.

Mother makes a tasty snack
and soup on the stove.

Everyone loves the hot
yummy soup and snack.

Do at Home

Tick the word-group / sentence that describes the picture.

1

☐ The boy is looking at a snail.

☐ The boy is looking at a snake.

2

☐ The letter has a stamp.

☐ The letter has a snack.

3

☐ The children have sweets.

☐ The children have snacks.

4

☐ The dog loves to sniff.

☐ The dog loves to swim.

5

☐ The swan is on the swing.

☐ The swan is on the snow.

-nt -nk -ng -ck

In this chapter, we will read about two consonant clusters -nt, -nk, - ng and -ck.

Read loudly and listen to the two consonant cluster sounds.

| a + nt = ant | i + nk = ink | ri + ng = ring | du + ck = duck |

 Here are some more new words for you.

 **-nt**

tent   cent   bent   vent

 **-nk**

pink   sink   tank   bank

-ng

king   swing   sing   string

-ck

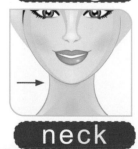   

neck   lock   pick   sick

Time to Solve

Look at the pictures and tick the cluster-sounds that the word ends with.

-nt
-nk

-ng
-ck

-ng
-nk

-nk
-ck

-nk
-ng

-ck
-nt

 Look at the pictures and circle their correct names.

duck lock

cent bent

ink sink

king sing

tent cent

pick neck

Circle the word not matching with the word-sound in its group.

tent   ink   bent

sink   king   pink

pick   sing   ring

lock   cent   neck

Write the words under the correct
cluster-sounds that the word ends with.

-nt

-ck

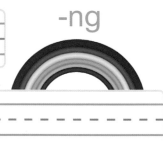
-ng

-nk

Match the sentences
to the pictures.

1.   The sled is on the snow.

2.   The ducks are on the swing.

3.   The cent is on the lock.

4.   The king sings.

Read the question and tick the correct option. Then write the answer on the line.

1 The boy opens what?
_____

lock

neck

2 The girl shows what?
_____

sing

ring

3 What is grey?
_____

tent

tank

4 What is in the desert?
_____

tent

cent

Circle the -nt, -nk, -ng, and -ck words and write them also.

1 The pink ink.
_____

2 The duck sings.
_____

3 The ant in the tent.
_____

Fill in the blanks and look at the pictures for clues.

1.　The _____ is carrying grain.

2.　She wears a _____ dress.

3.　Her _____ is very long.

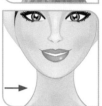

 Find the words in the boxes and write them. Look at the pictures for clues.

t	e	n	t	v	e

_____

r	r	i	i	n	k	b

_____

q	p	s	i	n	g

_____

t	r	p	i	c	k

_____

Time to Chant

My pink ring, my pink ring, I lost my pink ring.

Is it with the ant or is it with the king?

Is it under the sink or is it under the swing?

It is with the duck who got it by luck!

She wore it on her neck and started to sing.

Story Time

Read this story aloud.

Sight Words — the, an, in, of, a, to

The king loves music.

An ant sings in
front of the king.

The king loves the song.

The king gives a
cent to the ant.

Do at Home

Tick the word-group / sentence that describes the picture.

1.
   - ☐ The tent is pink.
   - ☐ The tent is black.

2.
   - ☐ The ring is in the sink.
   - ☐ The ring is under the sink.

3.
   - ☐ The duck is on the tank.
   - ☐ The duck is in the tent.

4.
   - ☐ The girl loves to sing.
   - ☐ The boy loves to sing.

5.
   - ☐ The cents are on the road.
   - ☐ The lock is on the road.

7

ch- -ch sh- -sh

In this chapter, we will read about two consonant clusters ch-, -ch, sh- and -sh.

Read loudly and listen to the two consonant cluster sounds.

| ch + ip = chip | ri + ch = rich | sh + op = shop | fi + sh = fish |

 Here are some more new words for you.

 **ch-**

chop   chef   chin   chick

 **-ch**

lunch   beach   bench   teach

 **sh-**

shell   ship   shark   sheep

 **-sh**

dish   wash   push   bush

Time to Solve

Look at the pictures and tick the
cluster-sounds that the word begins or ends with.

ch-
sh-

-ch
-sh

-sh
-ch

sh-
ch-

ch-
sh-

-sh
-ch

Look at the pictures and circle
their correct names.

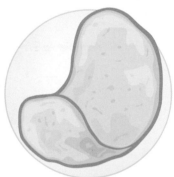

chin | chip

shop | ship

lunch | bench

wash | push

chop | chef

ship | shell

Circle the word not matching with the word-sound in its group.

chop   wash   chip

shark   beach   bench

ship   shell   chef

fish   lunch   dish

Write the words under the correct cluster-sounds that the word begins or ends with.

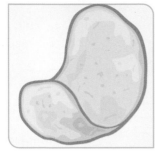

ch-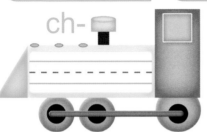

-sh

-ch

sh-

Match the sentences to the pictures.

1. The mole on the cheek

2. The rich boy

3. The big shark

4. The hot dish

Read the question and tick the correct option. Then write the answer on the line.

1 Who is cooking the food?
_____
- -

chef

chick

2 The kid is sitting on what?
_____
- -

bench

beach

3 What is on the roadside?
_____
- -

ship

shop

4 The girl eats what?
_____
- -

chips

dish

Circle the -ch, ch-, sh- and -sh words and write them also.

1 The (lunch) on the bench
_____
- -

2 The shark near the ship
_____
- -

3 The dish of fish
_____
- -

Fill in the blanks and look at the pictures for clues.

1. The _____ is full of children.

2. The _____ is closed for the day.

3. He has his finger on his _____ .

Find the words in the boxes and write them. Look at the pictures for clues.

| b | c | h | o | p | j |

| t | u | r | i | c | h |

| z | s | h | e | l | l |

| p | u | s | h | l | e |

Time to Chant

We went to the beach, the chef cooked a dish,

The dish was full of fish, I had it for my lunch,

Sitting on a bench, we saw a big ship,

And had potato chips.

Story Time

Read this story aloud.

Sight Words — it, is, the, boy, then, he, with

It is lunch time.
The boy is hungry.

He chops some fish.

He bakes the fish
with cheese.

Then he eats the dish quickly
with some chips.

Do at Home

Tick the word-group / sentence that describes the picture.

1

☐ The chef has made a dish.

☐ The chef is eating.

2

☐ The boy is sitting on the beach.

☐ The boy is sitting on the bench.

3

☐ The shark has big teeth.

☐ The shark has no teeth.

4

☐ The man is pushing the cart.

☐ The man is driving the cart.

5

☐ The boy is rich.

☐ The boy is poor.

th- -th ph- -ph wh-

In this chapter, we will read about two consonant clusters th-, -th, ph-, -ph and wh-.

Read loudly and listen to the two consonant cluster sounds.

th + ick = thick

tee + th = teeth

ph + oto = photo

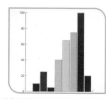

gra + ph = graph

wh + ale = whale

Here are some more new words for you.

th-
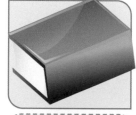
thick

-th

bath

cloth

ph-

phone

-ph

Ralph

nymph

wh-

white

wheel

whip

wheat

Time to Solve

Look at the pictures and tick the
cluster-sounds that the word begins or ends with.

   th- / ph-

   ph- / wh-

   wh- / ph-

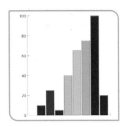   -ph / -th

   -th / -ph

   ph- / wh-

Look at the pictures and circle
their correct names.

whale | white

thick | thin

bath | teeth

photo | phone

white | wheel

graph | Ralph

Circle the word not matching
with the word-sound in its group.

white   thin   thick

cloth   photo   bath

phone   graph   Ralph

wheel   teeth   whale

Write the words under the correct cluster-sounds that the word begins or ends with.

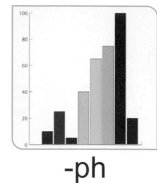

th-   wh-   -th   -ph

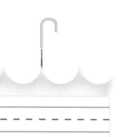

Match the sentences to the pictures.

1.   The book is thick.

2.   The boy is taking a bath.

3.   The girl is on the phone.

4.   The whale is big.

Read the question and tick the correct option.
Then write the answer on the line.

1 The girl is looking at what?

_____

- - - - - - - - - - - - - - - - - - - -

photo

phone

2 What is the boy showing to the girl?

_____

- - - - - - - - - - - - - - - - - - - -

graph

Ralph

3 What is black?

_____

- - - - - - - - - - - - - - - - - - - -

wheel

whale

4 The dog is showing its what?

_____

- - - - - - - - - - - - - - - - - - - -

teeth

cloth

Circle the wh-, -ph and ph- words
and write them also.

1 The white whale

_____

- - - - - - - - - - - - - - - - - - - -

2 Ralph with a graph

_____

- - - - - - - - - - - - - - - - - - - -

3 The photo on the phone

_____

- - - - - - - - - - - - - - - - - - - -

Fill in the blanks and look at the pictures for clues.

1. The girl is drawing a _____ .

2. The _____ is ringing.

3. Her T-shirt is _____ .

 Find the words in the boxes and write them. Look at the pictures for clues.

r   b   a   t   h   e

_ _ _ _ _ _ _ _ _ _ _ _ _ _

r   w   h   e   e   l

_ _ _ _ _ _ _ _ _ _ _ _ _ _

g   r   a   p   h   z

_ _ _ _ _ _ _ _ _ _ _ _ _ _

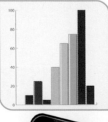

t   p   h   o   n   e

_ _ _ _ _ _ _ _ _ _ _ _ _ _

I am a big whale, I swim in the sea,

I have a thick tail, which moves with me,

My teeth are bright, and shine all the time,

They are strong and white, and always ready to bite.

Story Time

Read this story aloud.

Sight Words — the, up, to, of, and

Tring! Tring! the phone rings.

Ralph picks up the phone.

"Go and take the photo of the big white whale," says his boss.

Ralph goes to take the photo of the big white whale.

Do at Home

Tick the word-group / sentence that describes the picture.

1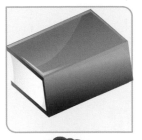

☐ The book is thin.

☐ The book is thick.

2

☐ The boy takes a bath.

☐ The boy cuts cloth.

3

☐ The photo is on the wall.

☐ The phone is on the wall.

4

☐ The graph is on the table.

☐ The graph is on the chair.

5

☐ The whale is in the water.

☐ The whale is on the wheel.

Let Us Revise 2

Look at the pictures and tick the
cluster-sounds that the word begins or ends with.

sm-
nk-

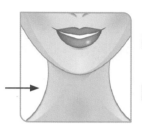
-ch
-ck

ch-
ph-

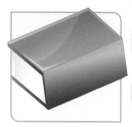
th-
sh-

-sh
-th

-ph
-ng

 See the picture and circle the correct word.

ship   king

Ralph   chef

whale   smile

rich   dish

shell   wheel

photo   lock

Fill in the missing letters.
Match the word to the picture.

| | | a | k | e |

| t | | | |

| | | i | p |

| | | e | e | l |

Match the phrase to the picture.

A small snail

A pink ship

A thin neck

A sweet dish

Fill in the blanks by choosing
the correct option.

 The swan loves to _____. (sweep / swim)

 The _____ is in the park. (swing / tent)

 The man is scratching his _____ . (chin / neck)

 The boy is looking at the _____ . (clock / globe)

 This wire is very _____ . (thick / thin)

Find the answers to these riddles by matching them to the pictures.

1   We talk through it.
What is it?

2   It is put on a finger.
What is it?

3   It lives in water.
What is it?

 Tick the sentence that describes the picture.

☐   The girl is smiling.

☐   The girl is crying.

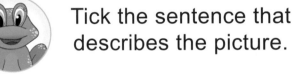

☐   The bench is white.

☐   The bench is pink.

☐   The beach is full of people.

☐   The ship is full of people.

Fill in the missing words choosing the two consonant clusters from the box to complete each story.

-ng, -ch, -nt, -sh, sh-, -th, ph-

Rolly and Polly went to the bea….. They saw lots of things at the bea….. They saw fi….. They saw a big ….ell. They took ba…. in the sea. They started to si….. and took ….otos with their camera.

sw-, sn-

Jim and Kim like to play in the ….ow. They picked the ….ow and made a snowball. They started to throw snowballs at each other. There they saw a ….ing. Jim climbed the ….ing and Kim had some ….eets.

Let's Review

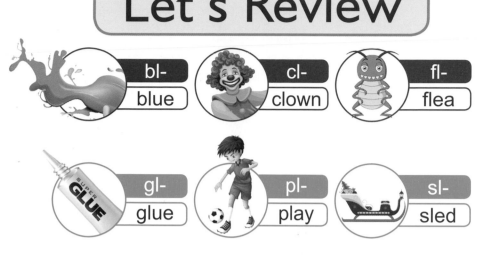

bl- blue	cl- clown	fl- flea
gl- glue	pl- play	sl- sled

br- bride	cr- crow	fr- fruit

dr- drum	gr- grape	pr- prince	tr- trunk

sm- smoke	sn- snow	st- steam	sw- swan

-nt ant	-nk ink	-ng ring	-ck duck

ch- chip	-ch rich	sh- shop	-sh fish

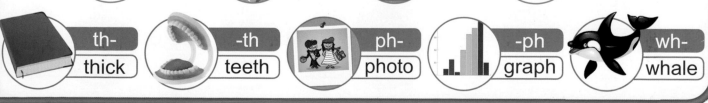

th- thick	-th teeth	ph- photo	-ph graph	wh- whale

Write the appropriate word in the same word sound box.

phone, chef, tent, smell, story, bath, drink, dish, snake, tree, glass, broom, tank, prize, thin, wheel, slide, frog, plant, lock, ship, grass, crab, nymph, flute, clip, blow, sweet, king, beach, push

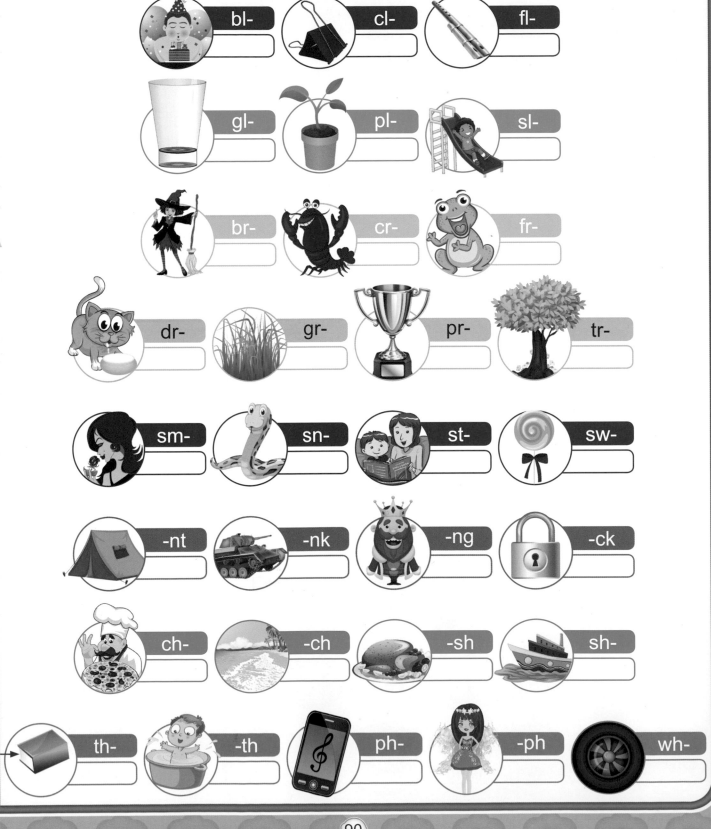

bl-

cl-

fl-

gl-

pl-

sl-

br-

cr-

fr-

dr-

gr-

pr-

tr-

sm-

sn-

st-

sw-

-nt

-nk

-ng

-ck

ch-

-ch

-sh

sh-

th-

-th

ph-

-ph

wh-

Let's Complete the Story

Use the words in the box to fill in the blanks.
Look at the pictures for the clue.

Jim is at the _____ . He is looking for a _____ . There he spots a big _____ near the _____ . He also sees a _____. He calls Nik, who is sitting on the _____ Nik comes and both the friends _____ together.

shell, ship, rock, beach,
whale, play, swing, duck

Super Square

Search the words ending / beginning with '-ch'

c	h	o	p	l
h	c	c	e	u
e	h	h	a	n
f	i	i	h	c
b	e	n	c	h

Now complete the following sentences with the words you searched in the Super Square.

1. The _____ _____ the carrot.

2. Tom's finger is on his _____

3. Stella is sitting on the _____

4. Jane is having her _____

Name the Picture

Circle the word that names the picture.

clock • clown

crate • crane

flower • florist

broom • branch

globe • glove

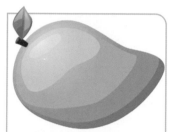

fruit • frame

plane • plate

slide • sled

drum • dragon

grape • grass

trap • tree

photo • phone

wheel • wheat

swim • swing

snail • snake

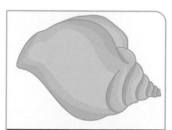

shell • shark

Picture Blender

Draw a line from the picture to its beginning letters.

sn

ch

sl

pl

cr

gl

sh

wh

Let's Fill It Up

Look at the pictures for clues to help you fill in the crossword puzzle. Also complete the sentences with the words you fill in the crossword puzzle.

She can _____

I can _____

Catty likes to _____

A _____ lives in the sand.

A _____ in a jar.

Picture Reading

Read each sentence given below saying the picture name as you read. Change each picture to a word and rewrite the sentence.

1. Water the

   _____

   _____

2. I love reading

   _____

   _____

3. A big green sat on a log.

   _____

   _____

4. I  my hands with soap.

   _____

   _____

5. The  gave a queen a

   _____

   _____

6. The door has a

   _____

   _____

7. A says, "Quack"!

   _____

   _____

8. I with my nose.

   _____